In the Days of

The Dinosaur Chase

Story by Hugh Price

Illustrations by Ben Spiby

One day,
Big Dinosaur chased Little Dinosaur
into a hole in a rock.

Big Dinosaur was very hungry.
He sat and waited
for Little Dinosaur to come out.

Big Dinosaur went on waiting
for a long, long time.

A brown lizard ran across the ground
and stopped to sit in the sun,
just outside Little Dinosaur's hole.

Big Dinosaur sat very still,
looking at the hole.

Big Dinosaur saw
Little Dinosaur's nose
come out
of the hole.

He saw
Little Dinosaur's head
come out.

Then Little Dinosaur
jumped at the lizard,

and Big Dinosaur jumped at Little Dinosaur ...

but Big Dinosaur was too slow.

Little Dinosaur raced away, just in time.
(So did the brown lizard.)

Big Dinosaur chased Little Dinosaur
in and out of the trees.
Big Dinosaur had great long legs.

Big Dinosaur could run very fast,
but the trees got in the way,
and he could not catch up.

Then Little Dinosaur
raced down to the ferns
that grew in the wet mud
by the river.
Big Dinosaur was
right behind him.
Big Dinosaur was so big
that he made
the ground **shake**.

Little Dinosaur jumped from fern to fern.
Then he ran across the mud.
Big Dinosaur chased him,

but Big Dinosaur was too big and too heavy.
His legs went down into the mud.
Big Dinosaur was stuck!

Big Dinosaur was stuck for a long time,
and so, once again,
lucky Little Dinosaur got away!